In Provence the plants that yield the oils cherished by aromatherapy lovers throughout the world grow in abundance. Above all, there is Lavender, which is cultivated on a large scale. But even more intriguing is that simply while strolling across the hilly slopes of Provence, one walks over half of what constitutes the aromatherapist's arsenal. Mountain Savory, Juniper, and Helichrysum all grow bountifully here. And then there is Thyme, the chameleon of the aromatic plants. Smelling the small Thyme plants growing in Haute Provence makes the chemotype phenomenon tangible. Their fragrance is nowhere near the smell a visitor from afar, who

aroma

Nr. 1/Winter 2000

knows the fragrance from imported oils, would imagine. Rather, it is an almost unbelievable mix of the most flowery terpene alcohol notes, more akin to the fragrance of the oil of Verveine or Rose than of the common hot and phenolic notes of Thyme. Judging by how popular aromatherapy has become in the industrialized Western nations, and by how much of it originates in Provence, it is tempting to think that more than just the physical substance of the essential oils travels throughout the world from its Provençal base. Also traveling with the oils is the spirit of connectedness with nature that permeates Provence. These oils carry with them a part of the savoir vivre of the region, connecting the user in faraway lands with Provence's inimitable sense of place. One could go a step further and consider

the inexplicable health benefits of the so called Mediterranean diet. For example, recent research has concluded that the 23 000 naturally occurring fragrant terpenoid compounds, the aroma of real food, are pivotal in cancer prevention. It is a short step to imagining that the essential oils of Provence are a means to let the rest of the world participate in the region's healthy lifestyle, laughter, joy, and history.

Contents:

Wild Perfume

From the viewpoint of agriculture most of the soil in Provence would be considered poor. "But how can this soil be poor when these perfumes grow on it?" asks Lucien, a local resident who gathers and distills plants that yield essential oils. Although the dryness of the land does not allow the plants to grow very tall, the

aromatic plants of Provence are the treasure of this land. They are small plants with extraordinary powers. "Most of their healing power, which is above and beyond that of cultivated oils, would be destroyed by even a little bit of nitrogen fertilizer," Lucien notes. Asked how he became involved with aromatherapy and essential oils, he answers, "By walking over the plants and smelling them."

Provence:
Land of Old

The climate and vegetation of Provence have been providing a gentle, nurturing environment to humans for more than 8,000 years. Some villages in Provence have been continuously inhabited since prehistoric times. Provence is known for products that delight the senses, from pastis and truffles to Lavender. In Provence lavender-blue window sills and brilliantly colored flowers turn the traditional stone buildings into soothing images of history and tranquillity. Traces of earliest Christianity as well as Roman and medieval monuments abound. History is palpable here, from Mary Magdalen's purported arrival in Marseille to the time of

Nostradamus, born in the city of St. Remy de Provence; from Bernard of Clairvaux being called the Consciousness of Europe, who popularized the Cistercian order in the 12th century, to the popes in Avignon; from the emergence of the university of Montpellier, where essential oils were first distilled in Europe, to the now closed Alcazar music theater in Marseille. Provence has something that is sorely amiss in today's world of anonymity and electronic isolation in which, some say, it does not matter where you are. In Provence there is a strong sense of place. And Lavender is its messenger.

5

Lavandin

The region of Provence is home to countless operations, large and small, which engage in the distillation and extraction of the indigenous aromatic plants and Lavender is the dominating crop, or so it appears. In reality it is Lavandin which provides the blue canvas for those picturesque shots which carry the romance of Provence all over the planet. Lavandin is cultivated and distilled industrial style to the tune of 1 000 tons of oil per year (1 000 000 liters). Industrial producers of household detergents and tooth-paste have a ferocious appetite for Lavandin oil. Lavandin essential oil is added to the commercial detergents to neutralize their somewhat unpleasant smell almost like a fragrance white-out, and allows the detergents to smell

neutral or be perceived as being free of odor.

A Hybrid called Grosso

In the 1970s the life span of the traditional Lavandin varieties dropped from 10 to 12 years to three or four years. After 1975 many fields were replanted with Lavandin Grosso, named after its discoverer Pierre Gross, who discovered it near the town of Apt. Grosso is robust and productive and its yield surpasses those of most other varieties. This variety currently covers almost 3/4 of all cultivated soil and represents 70% of the entire Lavandin production, up to 90% in the 'plateau' of Valensole.

The Ups and Downs of Lavender Production

In the early 20th century the harvest of wild Lavender was gradually supplanted by selection, cultivation, and agriculture, primarily in response to the increasing demand for Lavender from Grasse, a major center of perfume production.

Thus, cultivation of Lavender migrated from the alpine areas to the high plateaus of Provence. Yields of True Lavender reached a high point of an estimated 80-100 tons (90 percent still coming from wild Lavender) between 1920 and 1930. In the

early 1930s the first Lavandin crops emerged, turning out to be more advantageous for industrial cultivation. In 1950, 200 tons of Lavandin were produced. For the longest time Lavender was harvested manually by sickle and carried away

in a bag around the shoulder. Labor costs for the mostly Italian and Spanish migrant workers were relatively high in the 1950s, and this led to the first experiments in cutting the plants mechanically. Today the entire harvesting process is performed by machines, often allowing the farmer to harvest three rows of Lavender at a time. This accounts for the perfect symmetry of the Lavender plantations: six close rows of Lavender are separated by one broad row. In the year 2000 there are approximately 600 essential oil producers (in the Ardèche, Gard, Vaucluse, Drôme, and Alpes de Haute Provence) manufacturing 1 100 to 1 200 tons of Lavandin and approximately 25 to 50 tons of True Lavender.

Cousins and Clones

The vernacular term Lavender includes a number of species with very different properties. The term used in Provence for Lavande Fine, or True Lavender (Lavandula angustifolia or officinalis) is Lavande population. Each Lavande Fine plant is unique and has its own genetic heritage. Color, size, and fragrance vary from plant to plant, giving rise to the complexity and subtlety of the essential oil.

The techniques of cloning have led to a selection of varieties of Lavandula angustifolia with properties similar to those of Lavande population, yet with a higher yield and the ability to thrive at lower altitudes.

The two main varieties are the Maillette, a rustic and vigorous Lavandula angustifolia clone, and the Mathcronne, which yields an essence almost insoluble in alcohol. In Provence it appears that cultivation of the latter is being gradually abandoned.

Spike Lavender (Lavandula latifolia), which grows in warmer areas at lower elevations, has a much higher camphor content. Its uses in aromatherapy appear to have been much more limited than those of True Lavender. While the latter can be used as a general agent of health and lifestyle, Spike Lavender has been recommended in the literature for specific therapeutic interventions.

Spanish Lavender (Lavandula stoechas) has an even higher camphor content than Spike Lavender. In aromatherapy it is mostly avoided because of the feared, or real, toxic effects of its ketone components. It grows on the shores of the Mediterranean and is rarely found in Provence.

Lavande population
Population Lavender will show petals of varied colors, often on one plant.

Lavandin (Lavandula hybrida) is the hybrid product of True Lavender and Spike Lavender (Lavandula spica or latifolia). Lavandins are sterile plants with an oil yield five to six times higher than that of True Lavender. Their fragrances are dominated by camphor and are much less refined than those of Lavande Fine. The most common Lavandin is Grosso (L. hybrida grosso), which has all but replaced the Abrialis, which degenerated in the 1970s. Lavandin grosso is popular because of its lower camphor content and its fragrance, which resembles that of Lavande Fine. Lavandins are produced at industrial scale to serve as fragrance correctives for detergents and soaps.

Selecting for Power

Farmers try to select plants which give more and better oil. The clone shown here has not yet received a name and for now is called N-20.

Traditional Uses of Lavender Oil

Historical references point to a very broad spectrum of indications. The language of these older texts is far from the style of today's medical language and tends to make modern readers chuckle forgivingly about these ancient superstitions. Then again they could be pointers to realities which current day mechanistic approaches ignore. Some 18th century recommendations for Lavender:

Brain disease

10 to 12 drops of Lavender

Hysterical mood swings and vertigo

4 to 5 drops on an empty stomach

Migraines and to calm an upset stomach

4 to 5 drops on an empty stomach

Arthritis, paralysis and spasms

Lavender oil in infused oil of St. Johnswort.

Leaving the Fuseau or small Lavender filled bags in the closet is the traditional method to pefume clothes and laundry and to keep moths away.

The Data

Total Production of Lavandin :

Year	hectars	tons
1990	12 549	800
1998	13 279	1 020
1999	14 000	1 100

Total Production of Lavender and Clones:

Lavender is grown at altitudes between 800 and 1 500 m with limited yield, between 12 and 20 kg per hectar. The main clients for this oil are the perfume industry, aromatherapy and food processors. Lavandin yield lies between 80 and 120 kg of essential oil per hectar.

Year	hectars	tons
1990	2 604	35
1998	3 235	50
1999	3 500	50

Yield:

Lavandin: Grosso yields about 1.5 to 1.8%, 100 to 120 kilos per hectar, **Abrialis** and **Super** have even higher yields: up to 200 kilos per hectar.

Lavender fine: 0.6 to 0.7% which means 600 to 700 grams per 100 kilos of plant material. The yield per hectar never surpasses 25 kilos, the average yield is 15 kilos.

Lavender clone:

Maillette yields up to 40 to 60 kilos per hectar.

Dried plant material needed to distill one liter of essential oil:

Lavender fine: 120 kilos
Lavandin: 50 kilos
Grosso: 40 kilos
Super: 65 kilos

Area cultivated with Lavandin and Lavender in Haut Provence:

14 000 hectares of Lavandin
2 700 hectares of Lavender population
900 hectares of Lavender clone

Number of plants needed per hectar:

Lavender:

11 000 to 16 000 plants, planted at 0.4 to 0.5 meters apart and with 1.7 to 2 meters between the rows.

Lavandin:

7 000 to 10 000 plants, 0.6 to 0.8 meters apart, 1.7 to 2 meters between the rows.

Growing Altitude:

True Lavender produces the highest oil concentration at altitudes between 500 and 1200 meters. It is rarely found wild above 1 400 meters. It is cultivated at altitudes between 700 and 1 100 meters and in the Drôme even as low as 500 to 650 meters. At higher altitudes the fragrance of the essential oil of Lavender becomes more refined, yet the yield decreases.

Perpetually Popular

Domestic consumption and
export of Lavender oil far
exceed the amount produced
by agricultural methods. It
has become profitable to mix
less expensive essential oils
like Lavandin or Bulgarian
Lavender (from clones) with
synthetic linalool and linalyl
acetate and to offer the
resulting "bouquet" as True
Lavender. When the product
is shipped from addresses in
Provence, the deception is
slick enough to generate
more business than for the
real oil. In a local Provence
paper Henri Pouchon, the
president of the confrerie de
la lavande, states, "We produce about 50 tons of True
and clone Lavender, but
brokers end up exporting 250
tons. This is a greater miracle
than the ones of Lourdes and
Fatima together, where the
Virgin Mother has appeared
three times."

Phenomenon

The aim of Lavender adulteration today is seemingly not to create a product which is a deceivingly similar copy of the original. The aim has shifted. The reconstituted products which pose as true Lavender do not even attempt to smell like the real thing. They smell stronger. They are a dayglo version of the original subtleness, creating a bouquet many, who never smelled real oil would somehow expect. The way many of those concocted oils come across is supple, sweet and forceful. However, this has very little to do with the subtlety and refined elegance of real Lavender as it is distilled in the Provence. We observe a certain disneyfication of the oil, where the copy is louder and therefore 'better' than the original. The process is not unlike what has happened to California Chardonnay. Everyone talks dry, but the wines in the glass are sweet, fruity and oaky. The strategy obviously works for the mass market. The 'Grateful Dead' summed it up: "too much is just enough".

Detecting Adulteration

It comes as no surprise that the techniques of adulteration keep pace with the techniques of analysis. It used to be that the addition of Lavandin oils to true Lavender could be detected by the resulting elevated camphor concentration. Not anymore today there are bouquets on the market where the camphor content is not exquisitely low but low enough so it does not prove the addition of other substances. It used to be that the addition of synthetic linalool could be detected by traces of an impurity that came with it, dihydrolinalool. Not anymore. Today's synthetic linalool comes free of that impurity. But all is not lost. Lavandulyl acetate is normally present in True Lavender at a concentration of 2.5% to 4.5%. Lavandulyl acetate is not readily available and it is expensive. So very low concentrations of Lavandulyl acetate are often an indicator of adulteration. The same is true for concentrations of ocimene isomers in true Lavender. If they are much lower than 6% it often indicates adulteration. The specialized literature also reports that the ratios of key components, such as linalool to lavandulol can be utilized to identify adulteration. Finally enantio selective gas chromatography has become very useful. The linalyl acetate in Lavender is enantiomerically pure. Synthetic linalyl acetate is a 50:50 mixture of the two possible enantiomers. Addition of synthetic linalyl acetate is identifiable by the presence of significant amounts of the wrong enantiomer.

Distillation

Traditional distillation is gradually replaced by the 'vert-broye' method. Today about 70% of Lavandin is distilled this way. Without denying that most technological 'improvements' are mostly unstoppable, local expert Maurice Morard stays attached to the traditional 'en vase' method which, especially for True Lavender renders a finer product.

'En vase'

After being cut the flowering Lavender tops are tied into small bundles and left to dry for several days before the distillation. After the distillation the plant material is cleaned out of the alambic and serves as fuel for the next distillation. A 6 000 liter alambic will process about one ton of plant material. Average distillation time is 40 minutes and yields between 10 and 20 kilos of essential oil.

Vert Broyé'

'Vert Broyé' means shredding the green plants and immediately distilling them. This method produces a higher yield because loss of essential oil during the drying time is avoided. Supporters emphasize the quickness and higher yield of the process. Yet the method is not perfect because the composition of the distilled essential oil can vary depending on the degree of moisture in the plant material. The technique adds a green note to the fragrance of the oil which fades with time.

Where True Lavender Grows

While Lavender is on everyone's mind it is Lavandin which provides the blue canvas for the romantic images of Provence. In contrast to the Lavandin fields which present themselves ostentatiously the true Lavender, *Lavandula angustifolia* is more of a recluse. Fields of Lavande Fine or population Lavender, hide from the casual visitor. To see them one needs to search them out, know where to look, make a detour. The 'Lavande population' as the Provençale farmers call it, grows on top of the plateaux of the Haute Provence. It is concentrated but not exclusive to Saignon, Mont Ventoux and the plateau of Lagarde d'Apt. Significant Lavande fine areas are also found in the Drôme.

How much Monoculture?

If one were to develop an even-handed, educated, and reasonable response to the questions arising from the projections related to biotechnology, fields of Lavender hold subtle clues. The spectacular Lavandin fields please the eye and give high yields of essential oil. But their increased usefulness and improved manageability comes at a price, because they are sterile. The true Lavender populations hide out in higher altitudes. Underdeveloped plants live right next to plants that are big and thriving. Some have strong perfumes while others may not have any oil at all. Because of this diversity, the plants produce seeds that are able to take hold not only in ideal soil but also in less favorable spots. The hills and higher plains of Provence are full of thriving wild Lavandula vera plants. Because of their typically small size, these wild plants are not suitable for industrial uses. But they insure the constant renewal and adaptation of the species to its environment. The fields of Lavender population, Lavender clones, and Lavender hybrids offer

tangible and vivid examples for those who might be considering interventions into the very make-up of nature. They cover the range from exploitability, commercial usefulness, and homogeneity to vitality and diversity.

Above: Lavender and Everlasting growing wild.

Below: In fields of population Lavender every plant looks different.

Department Drôme

There are four Departments which share in the high plateaus of Provence: Vaucluse, Alpes de Haute Provence, Hautes Alpes, and Drôme. Many of the growers and distillers of the Drôme have embraced biodynamic agriculture, and cultivation of medicinal plants is a viable business. It is an often repeated story which says that when the '68 student revolt subsided many of the progressive minded Parisians took to the Drôme to realize their visions of a better world. If this is true the effort was quite success- ful. The Drôme valley has some exceptionally picturesque corners and preserving the natural environment is a generally accepted priority. The Drôme is home to the cooperative Plantes Aromatiques Du Diois and the Laboratoire Sanoflore. Both offer medicinal plants and essential oils. Important for aroma- therapy: From the Drôme comes true Melissa oil.

Mas de la Brune and its Garden

Provence is a land not of theme parks but of theme gardens. Among the most intriguing is the alchemical garden, the "Jardin d'Alchimiste", at Mas de la Brune, a beautifully preserved Renaissance mansion now converted into a hotel. Impeccable in style and amenities, the hotel is the perfect place to experience the enchantments of its magical garden, and the nearby village of Eygalières offers visitors a variety of Provençal restaurants and shops. The garden itself is actually a series of gardens, each with its own special aura and identity.

23

The concepts of the garden at Mas de la Brune are loosely based on medieval and alchemical writings. The garden presents the visitor with an environment that, through metaphors of alchemy, takes the conversion of lead into gold commonly associated with ancient alchemy to a much higher level, that of a spiritual quest. The parallel in a human's life is the evolution from mere existence to the full recognition of life's full and sublime meaning.

Signs posted throughout the garden greet the visitor with simple yet poignant directives and explanations:

Believer or disbeliever,
No matter who You are,
No matter what Your ambitions
Forget!

Have you heard about the alchemists?
Forget!
Use Your imagination,
Be attentive.

Alchemy, as presented in the garden, is the transformation of the soul through grace and initiative science. It is presented not as the "black magic" of old but as an essential tool of an era when being a great scientist also meant being a great philosopher, so intertwined were the two pursuits.

At the entrance to the garden signs proclaim:

Now that You know that alchemy is not an
Evil practice, You can enter these gardens
In search of the Philosopher's Stone.

You are entering true initiation.
Each garden represents a stage in the transformation of lead into gold,
or self-realization and renewal.

Form, composition, and ambiance of the garden
Express esoteric principles.
Begin this stroll with humor or with sincerity.
No matter what You choose,
Life has begun to change.

Follow into the Garden

At each new segment of the
garden visitors are greeted by
thought-provoking words of
greeting and inspiration:

The Black Garden

In this dark maze Your quest
begins.
Separate the pure from the
impure
under the reign of Saturn.

The material is symbolized by
the cipher 5,
The cipher of man,
and the number 11, represent-
ing beginning.
The element is salt.
The salt of Saturn is lead,
which the different passages will
transform into gold.

At the root of an oak tree
A black and dormant water:
The source of knowledge.
He who applies himself to it
may follow his path.

26

The White Garden

You can stay in the White all of
Your life.
As much as You wanted to leave
the Black,
the White can seduce You to
linger.

But You have to find the real
issue: to join the Supreme
Oevre,
Under the reign of the Moon,
reflected by a mirror of water.

The element is mercury,
Feminine and volatile.
She must get married to sulfur
to create the Philosopher's
Stone.
The cipher is 7, balance, and the
number is 2.

If You manage to free Yourself
from the Black,
using Your intelligence,
You then have to apply all the
strength of Your heart
to leave the White.

The Red Garden

Red, the Great Oevre
That transforms the most vain
into the most precious.
But genius and quality of heart
alone
Are never sufficient
To find the Philosopher's Stone.
It is also always a gift.
The Philosopher's Stone sym-
bolized by a fountain in the

center
gives access to the paths,
Which radiate out.
You go wherever You wish,
finally finding Yourself under
the reign of the Sun.
The element is sulfur.
Masculine and firm, it combines
with mercury so the Stone
arises.

The cipher is 9,
The highest cipher.
And the number is 33,
The one of universality.
Where Your quest ends
Your life begins.

The Ethnobotanical Gardens of Salagon

Ethnobotany studies the relations between humans and the plants around them. These relations are of diverse nature. They find their expression in the shape and design of agricultural lands, popular terminology for plants, the continued cultivation of fruit and vegetable species, knowledge and use of

plant drugs, the consumption of wild plant species or the technological exploitation of plants. The cultivation and processing of sugar cane in the early British colonies is an example for how deeply the fate of plants and cultures can be intertwined. In the traditional pharmacopoeia of Provence 170 plant species are well known and used. For today's standards this is an extraordinary high number.

Maison de la Biodiversité

The city of Manosque is home to another garden project Maison de la Biodiversité. The visitor is presented with plants from all over the world and explanations of the benefits of a diverse biosphere and also, what we lose if it were lost.

About aroma

Welcome to aroma. Essential oil use, mostly inspired by the various concepts of aromatherapy, has become quite popular in the last three decades. Under the umbrella of aromatherapy diverse influences merge. From scientific to esoteric and from subtle applications to dosages that might be labeled heroic, aromatherapy has defied categorization in conventional terms. aroma will not attempt to promote one approach over the other. Our purpose is to discover what is unique to the culture, science, and lifestyle that surround essential oils. aroma will not issue rules and recipes, even though the latter may be included on occasion. Instead, we want to take you on a journey, literally and figuratively, to discover those fascinating and alluring ingredients of essential oils and aromatherapy that cast a spell on so many. The starting point of the journey is marked by the realization that aromatherapy is unique in

the way it relates to science and technology. Essential oils are derived from relatively simple, intermediate-technology production processes. They appeal to feelings of naturalness and evoke back-to-nature themes. Used by humans for centuries, essential oils have attracted relatively little scientific or economic attention. This is compounded by the fact that essential oils are part of the "old economy." When viewed solely through the lens of commerce, they promise only moderate profits, if any. Consequently, the mainstream media and thus mass consciousness take little account of the substance of aromatherapy. In the occasional moment of media attention, aromatherapy is generally represented as a semi-serious, perhaps quaint modality. In today's fast-paced world, it lacks the appeal of technology and speed.

People's awareness of aromatherapy tends to develop outside the established rituals of the mass market, in which drugs are tested, touted, and sold.

Although practitioners of aromatherapy often seek links to science, most essential oil use comes about instinctively and intuitively. Aromatherapy generally escapes the admonitions of self-proclaimed watchdogs who caution against the folly of using what appear to be untested natural materials.

Even when the tools of science are applied in aromatherapy, many that are useful in understanding the chemical composition of essential oils fail to predict their most substantial effects. Apparently those effects are often mediated by their interactions with physiological components of what we call mind, consciousness, and emotions. Yet the structures and features of the molecules that render oils so powerful in their interaction with the chemistry of mind and emotions are difficult to grasp with the tools of experimental chemistry and pharmacology. Rather than using the manmade classification systems of chemistry, the interaction of essential oils with human physiology can be better understood by considering the powerful impact of random evolutionary selection.

Given that the evolution of life on the molecular plane is a consequence of specific enzymatic reactions, a clear distinction emerges between the effects of the natural and the synthetic. Throughout evolution enzymatic reactions in plants developed in a highly specific manner associated with the chemical substances present in the plant. The symmetry and component ratios of plant substances are difficult or impossible to copy in the laboratory. Lab substances are by definition expressions of human reductionism; they match or satisfy one parameter but are random in every other aspect. The products of laboratory synthesis, at least for the foreseeable future, will not produce a given substance in the exact way it is produced by enzymes in the living cell. Nor will it produce the same byproducts and trace components that result from the enzymatic reaction. Rather, the natural mix of molecules in a plant is a result of the plant's evolution and its responses to environmental and other influences. Most important, the reactions of plants to differences in the composition of light, mediated through photosynthesis, have no match among laboratory-produced processes. This is not to say that isolated synthetic molecules are not capable of interacting with physiological systems. But their interactions will be radically different from those of the mix of molecules from a natural plant extract, even if they share an important chemical component. In short, the effects of synthetics do not and cannot encompass the perfectly rounded interactions with mind and emotions that the rigors and trials of evolution have bestowed onto, for example, the essence of Lavender. In aromatherapy healing is induced not only by pharmacology but, more important, by the way essential oils change our perception of the world around us. Often a change in world view is what allows us to break destructive or self-destructive patterns or helps us to attain different stages in personal development. Although essential oils display straightforward effects—for example, anti-inflammative or sedative—it is their transformative qualities that are truly at the center of what we shall call here Tribal Aromatherapy.

Essential oils are intermediaries of a lifestyle that requires us and enables us to step back from the fads of the moment. For most people, a lifestyle that incorporates essential oils leads to a new view of reality, one in which manufactured substitutes for flavor, fragrance, art, and other aspects of the sensory world lose their importance and the original beauty of life can be rediscovered. All of this original beauty, from natural wildlife to the great achievements of human ritual, myth, and culture, is imbued with, and enhanced by, the fragrance of essential oils.

At the Abbey of Sénanque

Sitting down in the church of the abbey in contemplation can initiate unexpected shifts in the way how otherwise most inconsequential perceptions would affect the visitor. The austere, spartan architecture of Senanque somehow unmasks the monotony of modern media produced sensory impressions. It makes it obvious how media output exercises the most paralyzing and numbing influence onto the rise of spiritual ideas or perceptions. The simplicity of the walls and the absence of stimulation alter the perception of sound. Whispers are enhanced, foot steps sound more delicate, the commotion from outside becomes a gentle whisper and the noise of a chair being moved becomes a signal for the entrance of a new visitor. The world becomes a carpet and unimportant aspects disappear. Soft children's voices are clearly audible whereas shrieking conversations of travel stressed adults are swallowed by the invisible carpet.

Bernard of Clairvaux

Sense of Place is missing for many in modern society. In Provence Sense of Place is not in short supply. To the contrary the rich history heightens it, sometimes to levels that leave the unsuspecting traveler speechless. One such place is the abbey of Sénanque. Built in the quiet valley of a small stream it is again a place of spiritual devotion inhabited again by Cistercian monks. The spirit of the great Bernard of Clairvaux to this day informs prayer and spiritual direction of the monks. The stages of Bernards extraordinary life and the explosive growth of the Cistercian order under his leadership are vividly presented in a special display in the abbey. For everyone with only a modicum of sensitivity the attraction the mystic piety of this man has exerted on his contemporaries and even to this day is impossible to neglect.

Hildegard von Bingen's writings are often invoked when the historical use of herbs are discussed. The abbess called her work Physica "The Book of the inner disposition of the different qualities of creatures". Here are Hildegard's words on true Lavender, Spike Lavender and Melissa. True Lavender is warm and dry, because it has not much fluids. It does not work as food, but it has a strong perfume. And if a person infested with lice smells it often the lice will die. And its perfume clears the eyes. Spike Lavender (which Hildegard calls Wild Laven-

Hildegard's spiritual visions are preserved in her book Scivias, illuminated by extraordinary examples of early medieval calligraphy and drawing.

der) is warm and dry and its warmth is healthy. He who boils Lavender with wine, or if there is no wine, with honey and water and drinks it lukewarm will alleviate pain in liver and lungs and dampness in the chest, and will create for himself pure knowledge and a pure mind. Melissa is warm and people who eat it like to laugh, because its warmth touches the spleen and therefore pleases the heart. But someone in whom the white in the eye is growing, should tear from the ground the whole plant including the roots and submerge the freshly uprooted plant in pure well water and heat it in a bowl. And warm it shall be placed on the eye. This is repeated for three nights and the white in the eye will heal and disappear.

Looking at essential oils from a Chinese medical perspective is the significant contribution to western aromatherapy of Jeffrey Yuen. Mr. Yuen is an 88th Generation Taoist Master and has been immersed in the practice and study of Taoism and the classics of Chinese medicine since early childhood. Mr. Yuen applies the traditions of Chinese medicine that integrate physical, psychological and spiritual aspects to the therapeutic use of essential oils. Therapeutic possibilities arise from the realization that aromatherapy interacts with the senses more than other therapies, it changes our perception of the world. When disease is perpetuated by clinging to harmful patterns, oils are employed to alter pathological patterns towards healthier behavior.

To the Chinese herbalist the essence extracted from a plant represents its blueprint, containing the foundation of all energetic processes from growth to decline. This foundation is referred to as yuan-original qi. Essential oils are the extrapolation of this original qi of the plant and it is their very nature to influence conditions like breast cancer, but also other cancers, in which 'essence' (yuan qi) is implicated.

Further reading:
J. Yuen. Essential Oils in Chinese Medicine *in Proceedings of the 4th Wholistic Aromatherapy Conference, Nov. 10-12, 2000. San Francisco.*

No Proof:

A Tribal Way of Reckoning.

Tribal Aromatherapy

Contemporary Westerners generally learn about the therapeutic effects of medicines through science, which, ideally, proves that something works and shows how it works. In the case of essential oils, a different scenario applies. Although numerous in vitro studies have demonstrated the pharmacological effects of essential oils, rarely have those studies been transferred to clinical applications. Consequently, the impression persists that there is only scanty scientific proof of the effects of essential oils. People tend to learn about essential oils through informal exchanges and anecdotal information. In reality scientific reasoning does not play a central role in aromatherapy. Learning aromatherapy is often regarded as a form of prescientific study not unlike the ways in which our ancestors gained their knowledge of plant-based medicine. Although scientific explanations of aromatherapy are not numerous, aromatherapy nevertheless produces many stunning results. "Tribal aromatherapy," as the practice is referred to in these pages, presents different options for healing with essential oils. Some have been confirmed or suggested by science. The emphasis here, however, is on healing practices that are very real but outside conventional wisdom. Tribal aromatherapy explores the often astounding possibilities that have been discovered by those who have made essential oils a part of their lifestyle.

The information in these pages should not be considered in the same light as descriptions of conventional medical practices. Rather, the reports here describe the experiences of individuals or groups who have chosen alternative healing modalities, not officially approved or tested treatments.

Given this general caveat, typical consumer warnings, such as "never use oils undiluted" or "ingest oils only under the guidance of a qualified expert," will not be continually repeated. The absence of explicit warnings on every page does not mean that essential oils have no potential hazards, however. Many oils contain potentially toxic factors or components.

Further, substituting suggestions from this section for conventional medical methods is not recommended. Healing modalities are a matter of personal choice. Tribal aromatherapy does not make or imply statements about whether one modality is better than another. What may be highly beneficial to individual A may be useless or even detrimental to individual B.

Neither is tribal aromatherapy a substitute for conventional medical approaches. It is a noncommercial approach to healing based on re-establishing a balance with the natural world. It aims at strengthening the fabric of life rather than engaging in germ warfare. In essence, it explores how essential oils as biological agents interact with biological organisms.

Oils are no pills

The aromatherapy literature is full of disclaimers, and a distinct language of aromatherapy has arisen whose main purpose is to convey information about aromatherapy while not offending medical authority. Along with this language, a form of self-censorship has evolved in which proponents of aromatherapy do not actually report the effects of essential oils but instead explain that they are said to have an effect. Aromatherapy practitioners strive mightily to avoid claiming that essential oils are like drugs while at the same time implying that their effects are very much like drugs.

These elaborate verbal strategies overlook a basic point: Essential oils are not substitutes for conventional drugs or medical methods. They are not pills to be prescribed as a handy cure. They work best when they are used according to their own aromatic, liquid, lipophilic, and, ultimately, biological nature.

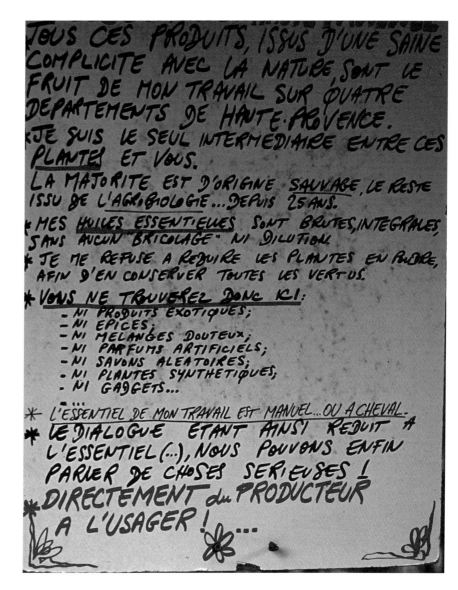

Provençale Aromatherapy Underground

The statements on this display represent the sentiments of distrust in commerce and trust in natural healing that can be easily found in Provence: "All products are made in partnership with nature and are the fruit of my labor in four departments of Haute Provence. I am the only intermediate between the plants and you. The majority of plants is of wild origin, the remainder from biodynamic agriculture, established for 25 years. My essential oils are pure, complete, no messing around, no dilution. To preserve all their virtues I refuse to grind plants to powder. Among my offerings You will not find: exotic products, spices, dubious blends, artificial perfumes, soaps, synthetic plants, gadgets. The essence: My work is done manually or with the help of a horse. The dialogue is therefore reduced to the essential and we can finally talk about serious matters".

Tribal Uses

In textbook aromatherapy the simpler uses of Lavender oil dominate. It effectively ameliorates the often violent and painful consequences of burns and insect bites, it closes and heals small wounds. Beyond that it benefits body and soul almost by default. We are lacking instruments and language to describe its true benefits. But instinct overrides these shortcomings. Everyone who knows it comes back to this oil forever. Humans, at least in the western, societies crave Lavender. Trusting instinct often is life saving.

Lavender population and also the clones are tolerated extremely well internally, on skin and on mucous membranes. Tribal aromatherapy uses the oil often and liberally. As with other oils the chemical structure of its known components does very little to explain the full

range of its physiological and psychological benefits. Difficult to pinpoint, but definitely there.

Despite its universal appeal exploring Lavender is a highly individual experience. There is a preference for the subtle and elegant population Lavenders among those who had the opportunity to play with the various oils. It appears reasonable that the complexity of the population oils, which expresses the plants capacity to adapt, transfers exactly this quality, namely the power to adapt. In this fashion Lavender produces deep and refined longterm benefits. At the same time farmers in Provence, who regularly work with Lavandins, swear that even the simplest Lavandin oil will cure many of their every day complaints.

Essential Oils
and the Liver

Recent research has demonstrated that essential oil components have direct influence on vital processes in the liver. It is well established that terpenoids induce liver detoxification enzymes. Scientific publications have come from researchers at the University of Wisconsin, Madison and other universities. Reviewing these scientific findings along with and next to described traditional uses of, for instance, Lemon in Traditional Chinese Medicine or Rosemary oil in classic aromatherapy reveals a rational basis for the traditional recommendations to use essential oils to induce the removal of toxins from the liver. Detoxification induced by essential oils is a phenomenon often alluded to in aromatherapy literature, but mostly in rather vague terms. The realization that essential oil components have distinct influences on the induction of Phase I and Phase II liver detoxification enzymes allows a closer

correlation between tradition and research. It is clear that the potential of essential oils to be beneficial for different aspects of liver metabolism is barely tapped into. More generally speaking, finding scientific proof for traditional or ethnopharmacological concepts is not rare. Scrutinizing published research, it appears that finding proof is not a question of whether the traditional approach really works. Instead it depends on the direction of the research and the original intent to prove or disprove the efficacy of plant remedies.

Provençale Herbs have different influences on the liver. Lavender slows down the release of glucose, prevents bloodsugar lows. Rosemary stimulates the elimination of toxins and the release of glucose. Everlast jumpstarts the organ in a condition the French call Crise de Foie. The essential oil of wild Carrot seed is unusually mild to the tastebuds. It regenerates and strengthens the liver, especially after assault from viruses or toxins.

Everlasting

properties. There is practically no skin condition which would not benefit from Helichrysum oil. From making scars disappear to the prevention of hemorrhages after injuries Helichrysum oil works for long term

The story of the essential oil of Helichrysum italicum is one of unstoppable popularity. It illustrates well the forces at work in contemporary aromatherapy as its superb qualities were indeed discovered and explored by the modern aromatherapy movement. Helichrysum oil is barely mentioned in the early aromatherapy books, but at some point during the mid 1980s its reputation began to soar. What was once a commodity exclusively produced for the fragrance and flavor industry in Grasse was discovered to be an almost miraculous therapeutic agent. Its ascent began with an increased awareness for its incomparable antiinflammative and regenerative

and deep tissue healing as well as for immediate pain relief. A major part of its success is that it is so easy to use. Simply applied topically, neat or diluted in a base oil or in another antiinflammative essential oil, it is always gentle. And it always works. The chemical composition of the oil is rather well known. A landmark study of P.

The main classes of components present are sesquiterpene hydrocarbons and terpenoid esters. Diones, rather uncommon in essential oils are also found. The nature of these components which make up the bulk of Everlasting oil is concurrent with its anti-inflammative and possibly its regenerative properties, but it does not explain how these effects can be so strong, so pronounced in this oil. Nor does it explain its anti-hemorrhaging effects, and its ability to prevent tissue from being traumatized. The effects of Helichrysum oil are immediately obvious to everyone who researches it in earnest. It is remarkable that the effects and uses of Helichrysum oil became established merely through exploration by lay users. There is no substantial research on the pharmacological effects of this oil. Its large catalog of indications was compiled without the help of science.

A comprehensive study of the components of Helichrysum italicum oil has been published by P. Weyerstahl. 1986. *Isolation and synthesis of compounds from the essential oil of Helichrysum italicum* in Progress in Essential Oil Research (E.-J. Brunke, ed.). Walter de Gruyter, New York.

Weyerstahl identified a wide range of its main and secondary components, many of which were identified for the first time.

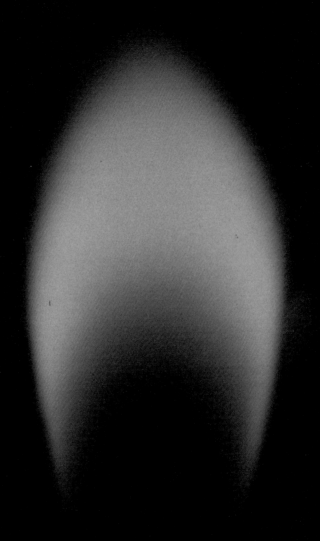

BURNS

Aromatherapy's answer to small burns is Lavender, German Chamomile and ice cubes. Keeping the burnt spot cold with an ice cube and keeping Lavender on the lesion as long as the pain persists will do wonders. Even in cases where the top layer of the skin has come off from the lower lying tissue, often times it will be 'back on' the next morning. Essential oil of German Chamomile (Matricaria recutita) of the (-) alpha bisabolol type will do the same trick.

Worried about your Teenagers, STD's?

Studies in the past have unambiguously demonstrated that many diverse essential oil components have anti-viral, anti-bacterial and anti-fungal properties. A study most relevant for aromatherapy was published in 1987 in the German language by R. Deininger and A. Lembke. It was presented again in 1995 in San Francisco and can be found, in the English language, in the Proceedings of the 1st Wholistic Aromatherapy Conference, San Francisco (1995).

Attitudes towards sex are often driven by rather different moral and cultural notions. As representatives of aromatherapy try to conform and not to ruffle feathers, issues of sex and sexual hygiene are rarely raised. Because of this, some of the most beneficial applications of essential oils have gone sorely underreported. Essential oils can be and are used with great ease and success to improve sexual and/or genital hygiene. The precondition for using essential oils on genitals is that they are non-irritant and anti-inflammative. Experiences of the tribe, as in tribal aromatherapy, but also of French physicians, such as aromatherapy icon Dr. Daniel Pénoël, show that if non-irritant anti-viral and anti-fungal oils, highly diluted in a suitable base oil, are used for personal hygiene and during sexual activity, the incidence of genital irritations and infections is sharply diminished. Given the highly anti-viral nature of many essential oils, logic would dictate that using essential oils during sexual activity would decrease or even prevent the transfer of viruses. Using essential oils on the genitals is good hygiene and esthetically pleasant.

Essential oils which are seemingly best suited and most pleasant are Everlasting (Helichrysum italicum), True Lavender, (only authentic from distillation, adulterated oils may irritate) and Rose in combination with Lavender and/or Everlasting. If more a more therapeutic or technical approach is desired, Hyssop off. var. decumbens and the softer geraniol and linalool types of Thymus vulgaris oils can be considered. The above is not meant to be uncritically implemented. It is meant as food for thought and as a point of departure for exploring a less complicated lifestyle.

Notes from the Aromatherapy Underground: Hepatitis C

Maybe not surprisingly the purest forms of idealism are found among the one woman or one man herb gatherer-distillers in Provence. Some sell their oils and herbs locally to customers who use them medicinally. On this local level aromatherapy is closest to its original promise: Healing from nature. The commerce driven aspects of British and American aroma therapy are refreshingly absent. Instead of pastel packaging there are hand written labels. More importantly the bottles contain oils of unparalleled radiance, wild crafted from the so called meager soil of Haute Provence. Distiller and client are aware of the exceptional powers vested in these oils. Their pristine purity and authenticity are not even used as selling points. Instead the parties involved are united in the belief that the oils from wild plants have qualities not found in cultivated oils. In rural France individuals can be found who dare to resist the subtle and less subtle pressures to conform. To them it is only logical to look for new answers where the conventional ones fail. Hepatitis C and also B are such a case. In this environment aroma has learned of a successful treatment of this condition with wholistic measures, mental and spiritual renewal and essential oils. Key oils in the treatment were Clary Sage from biodynamic cultivation, wild Rosemary, wild Carrot seed and Buxus sempervirens (dried leaves and essential oil. This drug is toxic, safe dosages for the oil have seemingly not been published). The oils are part of an all encompassing treatment and are ingested for four days and then paused for ten days. Then the cycle is repeated.

No dosages are given here. The above is not intended to be used as recipe but as food for thought. Adopting a regime like the above with hopes for a magic bullet will almost always fail. As stated throughout aroma, expecting essential oils to 'work' as if they were elements of the conventional medical model is a prevalent misconception even inside aromatherapy circles. To try these methods one has to embark on a journey which may not be easy but could already be part of the healing. It involves listening to critical opinions, reevaluating lifestyles in consumer society and questioning processed foods. Most likely it even involves questioning progress and technological acceleration as it chips away at the very foundations of our physiological and emotional and spiritual existence. Stepping outside the conventional medical routine may not be as irresponsible, as the guardians of the status quo will claim, but it also may not be for everyone.

Verveine

Verveine or Lemon Verbena (Lippia citriodora) has one of the most radiant fragrances and one of the most complex compositions among commonly available essential oils. Franchomme and Pénoël's *l'aromathérapie exactement* lists an interesting catalogue of indications for this oil, which includes fearfulness, depressions, entero colitis and Crohn's disease. It is interesting to note that an oil which uplifts the spirit finds applications for conditions associated with contemporary material lifestyles. In a development typical for aromatherapy individual patients simply tried the oil and observed. Some say they derive benefits and continue to use it. No adverse reactions have been reported in the aromatherapy literature, despite the oil's content of potentially photosensitizing furocoumarins.

Oils from wild Plants

Cultivation must be the answer for producing essential oils for the world. Only through cultivation can the large quantities be generated a growing worldwide market absorbs. But when it comes to addressing the serious diseases of our time oils from wild plants have the most power to reverse the damaging effects of civilization.

Even the largest suppliers of consumer goods ponder how to integrate organic components into their products to be able to print the coveted designation prominently on the labels of their merchandise. Commercialization threatens to chip away at the real meaning of the concept and turn it into an empty phrase betraying the original intent. The trend towards different degrees of organic is likely to intensify. There will be organic which simply satisfies applicable legal requirements and there will be organic attempting to be better, closer to nature and more true to intents of protecting biodiversity. The differentiation among the various certifying bodies reflects that trend. To help clarify aroma presents statements of purpose some of these organizations provide upon request. The tone of the given information provides an extra level of insight.

Commercial ?

Ecocert

has become a dominating certification organization especially in the area of the EU. Its objectives and style are geared towards providing a reliable certification process in today's commercial environment. Information provided by Ecocert contains, among others, the following statements: Ecocert Belgium is a registered inspection and certification body that verifies the conformity of organic products with the European organic regulation (CEE) 2092/91 and national norms. Ecocert, founded more than 15 years ago, is an international network operating in Europe, Africa, Asia and America. Ecocert group controls more than 20 000 producers and 2 000 food-processing establishments. Formal agreements are drawn up between Ecocert and certification applicants before the certification process can begin. According to the information given by the applicant an inspection plan and a cost estimation are agreed upon. Provided with such information the appropriate inspector chosen for each inspection, carries out an on site visit. Agricultural units, parcelles and crops are visited, fertilization and pest and disease control are checked, animal keeping is observed and storage premises and bookkeeping are controlled. Processing plants mainly have to prove conformity regarding processing technologies and recipes, guarantees of raw materials and ingredients, products quantity balance and traceability of products by a sophisticated audit trail. Label checking and, if necessary, sample taking for scientific analysis in accredited laboratories is part of the inspection program. The findings are recorded in a detailed inspection report which is exclusively destined to the applicant and to the certification staff of Ecocert. Certification consists of comparing the inspection findings with the regulation requirements. Conformity, and if necessary, amelioration demand are stated in a written certification decision and a certificate is submitted to the conforming applicants. This process of certification allowing progression and evolution towards full conformity of products is completely independent and impartial. Furthermore all information is kept confidential as part of written agreements by all parties involved.

CCOF

The California organization for organic farming includes these statements in the information it provides: What is Organic? Organic refers to methods of growing and processing foods that rely on the earth's natural resources. Pests and weeds are managed using earth-friendly means such as beneficial insects and mechanical controls. Organic farmers work to build natural nutrients in soil which help fertilize plants without reliance on synthetic fertilizers. Organic Production: Offers food produced within nature's own balanced and fertile system. Helps keep our air, soil, and water free of toxic chemicals. Ensures that animals are humanely raised, without synthetic hormones or antibiotics, and only fed organic feed. What is Certified Organic: Products labeled "certified organic" have been grown and processed according to strict standards. CCOF annually inspects farms and facilities to ensure that no harmful chemicals have

been used for at least three years, that foods are processed using sustainable methods, and that growers and processors keep detailed records of their practices. The 2000 CCOF handbook contains all of our standards that paved the way for organic farming legislation like the California Foods Act of 1990. CCOF was the first organization to certify farms in North America, continually leading the way by promoting sustainable agriculture since 1973.

S.I.M.P.L.E.S.

(Syndicat Inter Massifs Pour La Production Et L'Economie Des Simples)

This organization preserves the use of medicinal plants as it has been historically known in France since the late Middle Ages. Its objectives are to maintain a supply of natural remedies in this tradition, with an emphasis

or organic

Demeter

on simplicity and affordability. For medicinal plant cultivation the Simples code requires to plant and cultivate medicinal plants as close as possible to their natural, wild conditions, so their character is not altered. Fields need to be away and protected from polution sources like factories or autoroutes. Biological agriculture excludes all synthetic chemicals, such as fertilizers or herbicides. Previously treated soil has to be without chemicals for three years. Motorized machines are permitted for the preparation of the soil. Animal pulled utensils are permitted throughout the production. The use of motorized machines is only allowed until one month before the harvest. Water quality has to be guaranteed. Plants from naturally dry environments, such as Thyme, Rosemary, Savory, Lavender, Hyssop, Sage or Oregano may not be watered.

The Demeter Association, Inc. certifies farms as Biodynamic. Biodynamic agricultural principles emphasize living soil and the farm as a wholistic organism. The name of the Greek goddess of agriculture was chosen in the late 1920s by Biodynamic farmers in Europe to represent their products in the marketplace. Demeter mythology has its roots in the earlier Isis mythology of Egypt. At one level the Demeter myth speaks metaphorically of the seasons, of the cyclic end of the agricultural season each fall, and attendant wait through the winter for spring's renewal with new crops. At another level, the myth embodies a more profound awareness of the deeper mysteries of the human soul. The mission of the Demeter Association is to foster, encourage, and improve Biodynamic methods and practices by certifying growers, processors, and manufacturers of Biodynamic foodstuffs. Demeter operates exclusively for agricultural and horticultural purposes. Demeter certifies farms as either Biodynamic, or in conversion to Biodynamic.

Monsieur Lavandin

In the little town of Simiane la Rotonde not much happens, at least not with regard to Lavender, that Alain Cassan does not know about. He is the president of the Société Coopérative Agricole Des Plantes À Parfum De Provence and also mayor of Simiane. Monsieur Cassan has Lavender in his blood. His grandparents were among the first to begin cultivating Lavender on the plains of Haute Provence around the year 1915. Needless to say, his son cultivates Lavender too. M. Cassan has overseen a tremendous expansion in the production and marketing of Lavandin oils from the cooperative. An important part of this development was to educate and convince the industrial buyers about pure oils. The motto of the cooperative is transparency. The planted areas as well as the stills are in plain view and visitors are welcome at the warehouse of the cooperative. With this the coopcrative has been very successful in supporting its farmers. But an even higher priority is placed on the quality of the product. Besides the enormous amounts of Lavandin oil, the cooperative produces about eight tons of Lavandula angustifolia from population and clones. The oils from different farmers are kept separate and prospective buyers can sample the various lots and choose their barrel.

Alain Cassan

Professeur d'Aromathérapie

The Domaine des Arômes is testimony to the strong connection that exists between humans and aromatic plants in the Drôme valley. Bright modern architecture houses the operations of Laboratoire Sanoflore, including a small restaurant. The main attractions for the visitor are a well established aromatic garden and a highly original store with the products of the Laboratoire and a most unusual collection of plant paraphernalia. Sanoflore has been around for quite some time and is one of the pioneer enterprises of the early days of French style aromatherapy. Rodolphe Balz, founder, mentor and vice president came to aromatherapy after being professor for biology, sociology and geography at the university of Geneva. His observations of gifted therapists using essential oils in the most subtle ways with astonishing results stimulated him to shift the focus in his professional life. Those

Rodolphe Balz

properties in essential oils which may be so subtle and powerful at the same time that science simply has not found the right means to explore and describe them. Laboratoire Sanoflore continues to put out essential oils and consumer products which reflect its commitment to organic agriculture.

healings which were real but defied the basic explanations of scientific methods attracted him. Given his background he is not inclined to explain these phenomena with esoteric terminology or a belief in magic. Instead he concludes that there must be

Everything Organic

Michel Meneuvrier oversees the operations of the cooperative 'Plantes Aromatiques Du Diois' in Vercheny. The cooperative specializes in biodynamic cultivation of essential oils and medicinal plants. The Drôme valley provides ideal conditions for the cultivation of Lavender, various chemotypes of Thyme, Tarragon or organic Peppermint to name only a few. The latter oil is a rather uncommon product. It is laborious to maintain organic Peppermint cultures and bona fide

Michel Meneuvrier

organic Peppermint oil is rare. The cooperative also produces dried herbs of St. Johnswort and Calendula. Maybe most notably, they have perfected the art of cultivation and distillation of Melissa. In a relatively small still they produce the oil in 100 to 200 ml amounts per pass. Running the still more or less 24 hours a day yields between 40 and 80 kilos annually.

61

Addresses

Destinations, Distilleries, Professional Organizations

Musée de la Lavande
Route de Gordes
F-84220 Coustellet
Tel. +33 4 90 76 91 23
Fax +33 4 90 76 85 52

Gardens:

Jardin de l'Alchimiste
Mas de la Brune
F-13810 Eygalières
Tel. +04 90 67 67
Fax +04 90 95 9921

Musée de Salagon/ Conservatoire Ethnologique de la Haute Provence
F-04300 Mane
Tel. 04 92757050
Fax 04 92 75 70 58

Jardin des Arômes
Promenade de la Digue
Nyons
Tel. 04 75 26 04 30

Jardin des Lavandes
Sault
Tel. 04 90 64 14 97

Distilleries:

Société Coopérative Agricole Des Plantes Aromatiques De Provence
Contact: Margrit Müller
Maison Pazery
Route de Nice
F-04320 Entrevaux
Tel. +33 4 93 05 48 03
Fax +33 4 93 05 48 21

Plantes Aromatiques Du Diois
F-26340 Vercheny
Tel. +33 4 75 21 73 16
Fax +33 75 21 75 34

Sanoflore
Parc Naturel Du Vercors
F-26400 Gigors-et-Lozeron
Tel. +33 4 75 76 46 60
Fax +33 4 75 76 46 38

Bleu Provence
Promenade de la Digue
Nyons
Tel. 04 75 26 10 42

Coopérative Lavande des Alpes
Rosans
Tel. 04 92 66 60 30

Lavande 1100
Lagarde d'Apt
Tel. 04 90 75 01 42

Professional Organization:

CRIEPPAM
Z. I. St. Joseph
Traverse de Métiers
F-04100 Manosque
Tel. +33 4 92 87 70 52

Organic Certification:

Syndicat SIMPLES - Fosse
F-662200 Saint Paul de
Fenouillet

For the certification of
products inside CEE
France: Ecocert sarl
BP 47
F-32600 L'Isle Jourdain
Tel. 33 5 62 07 34 24
Fax 33 5 62 07 11 67
e-mail: ecocert@iway.fr

Demeter Association,
Britt Road, Aurora NY
13026

Travel in Provence:
Les Routes de la Lavande
2, avenue de Venterol
BP 36 - 26111 Nyons
Tel. 04 75 26 65 91
Fax 04 75 26 32 67

**California Certified
Organic Farmers**
1115 Mission
St. Santa Cruz, CA 95060
Tel. 831 423 2263
Fax 831 423 4528

Ecocert Belgium
1 Chemin de la Haute
Baudecet
1457 Walhain
Tel. +32 081 60 03 77
Fax +32 081 60 03 13
e-mail: info@ecocert.be

A sourcebook of
Provençale knowl-
edge of wild herbs, by
the ethnobotanist of
Salagon:
**Le Livre des Bonnes
Herbes**. Pierre
Lieuthaghi. Acte Sud.
ISBN 2 7427 0953-3.

A gentle Lavender
book: **The Lavender
Garden**. Robert
Kourik. Chronicle Books

Overheard on the
local markets,
quotes from the
Provençal Under-
ground:

Wild Lavender re-
cedes, populations
are only half the size
of what they used to
be. In the past Laven-
der plants used to
live between 15 and
50 years. Now they
die after 4 to 10
years.

The fragrance of
Thyme always
changes, with the
year, the season, the
time of the day. It
smells like Rose in
the morning and like
Verbena in the
evening.

Young people are
useless for the har-
vest. Everything
stings, thorns, the
sun, the bees.

The Bouquet makers
import Lavender
from China for ff 160.
This is the new face
of essential oil pro-
duction.

Look for aroma 2 in August 2001

The main topic of aroma 2 will be essential oils from Morocco, Tunisia and Spain. These oils are messengers of hot desert sun and heavenly gardens, of the peaceful coexistence between Christian, Moorish and Jewish culture in the 8th century Al Andalus and

the wisdom and art of scholars and artists who migrated there from the courts of Baghdad and Damascus. To this day Moroccans live in close contact with nature. Neroli and Rose, Peppermint and Saffron are floral and culinary aromatic expres-

sions of this part of the world. From the Atlas mountains come oils which prevent the loss of fluids and protect against the intensity of the sun. These oils close internal and external wounds. Oils from the barren fringes of the Sahara desert open the soul for spiritual development.

aroma

No.1 / Winter 2000
aroma is published in loose sequence by Terra Linda Scent and Image Inc. (TLSI), POB 903, San Rafael, CA 94915. USA

Contributors to this Issue:
Carole Addison, Rodolphe Balz, Resa Blobaum, Alain Cassan, Matt Durst, Julien Haas, Sean McCoy, Michel Meneuvrier, Margrit Müller, Jesse Ramirez, Hank Resnik, Jennifer Tescallo, Reyna Ventula.

Photography and Design:
Monika Haas, Kurt Schnaubelt

Distribution:
Pacific Institute of Aromatherapy
POB 6723, San Rafael, CA 94903. USA.
Tel. +1 415 479 9121
Fax +1 415 479 0119

Price (US): $ 33

Scans: TLSI

Printing:
Performance Printing Center
San Rafael, CA

© **2000**
TLSI, San Rafael